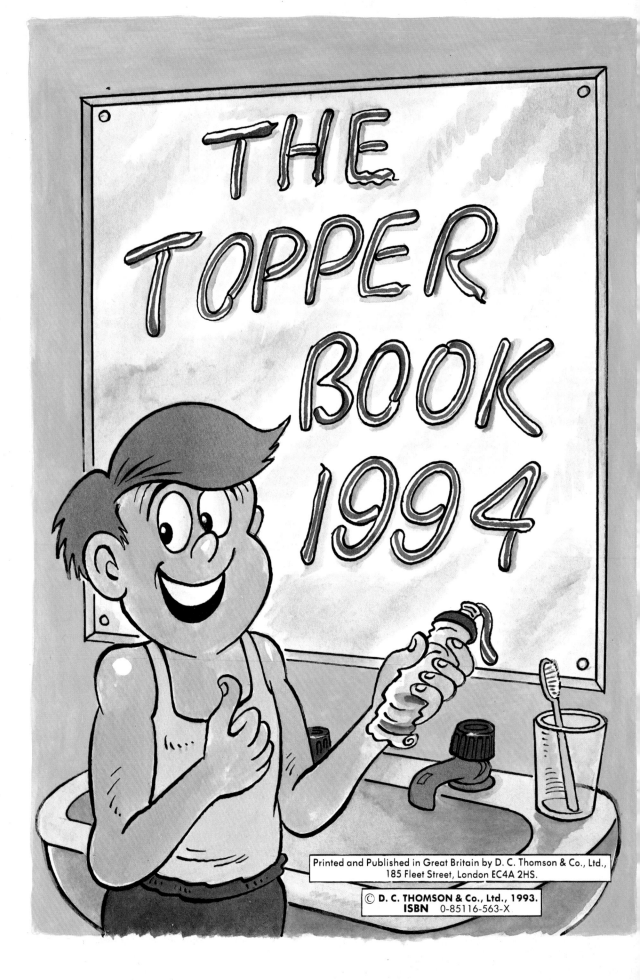

Printed and Published in Great Britain by D. C. Thomson & Co., Ltd.,
185 Fleet Street, London EC4A 2HS.

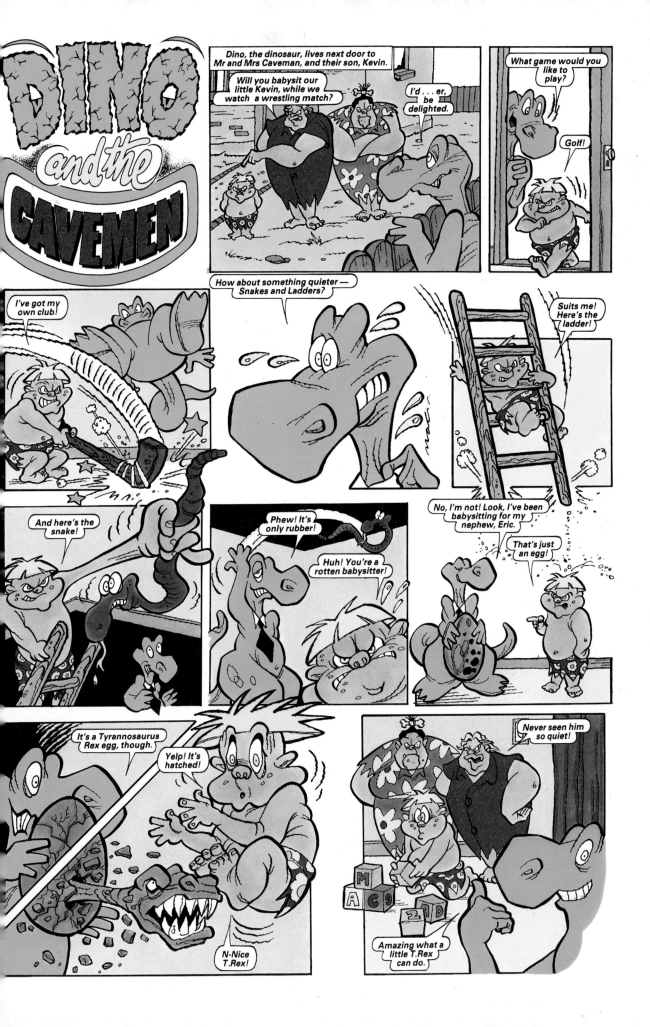

THIS joke!

It was worth it for the laugh.

Oh, well.

POSTMAN DELIVER TO CONVENTION

For us?

POSTMAN DELIVER TO CONVENTION

I'll just check for stowaways.

POSTMAN DELIVER TO CONVENTION

Dicky. I thought so.

Yikes!

POTSWORTH and Co., in "SNOW JOKE".

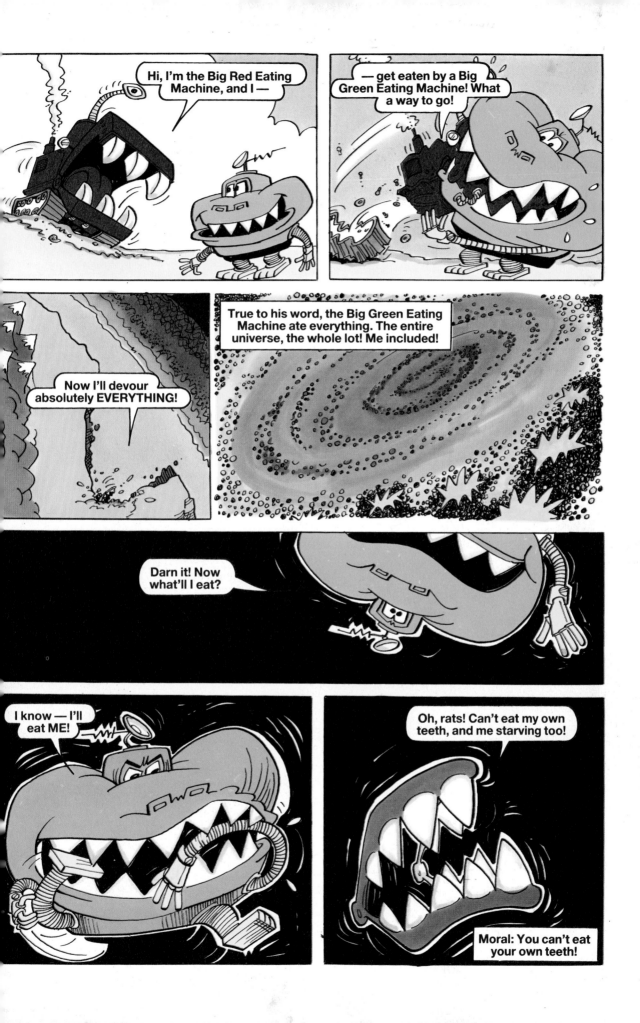